I am Lotty.

I am a puppy.

Look at me.

1

Look at me
in the mud.

Look at me
on the log.

Lotty looks at the
big cat in the box.

Lotty looks at the
hen in the hut.

Lotty looks at the
fat cat on the mat.

Lotty looks at the
fat frog in the mud.

I am Lotty, the
happy puppy.
Look at me.